What's In This Book?

1	How-to news page
1	W page for Where When Who What & Why
1	1/2 writing page 2 get you on your way
1	Good Time clock chart
9	pages & a dog-shaped map 2 write on
1	drawing page
3	writing pages & a 2-page river 2 write on
20	writing pages with 3 drawing pages mixed in
1	poem page & 2 last writing pages
2	food pages
2	Signs & Place Names pages
2	License Plates & Bumper Stickers pages
1	Souvenirs & Gifts page
1	Packing List page
2	Best & Worst (or, Magnifique & Urp) pages
2	Counting Things & Sights pages
2	New Friends & Autographs pages
1	Friends' Addresses page
3	storage pockets: Photos, Post Cards, & Ephemera
4-page	fold-out map (with 4 pages on the back)

ONE MILE   ONE SMILE

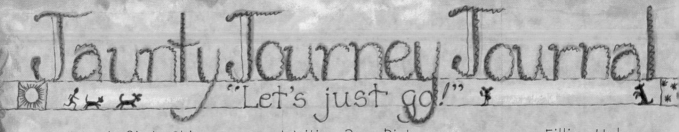

Jaunty Journey Journal
"Let's just go!"

Wordy Birdy Chirps

Nothing's more perfect than a travel diary if you love words! Get this: <u>daily</u> – every day; <u>diary</u> – a daily record; <u>diurnal</u> – daily; <u>jaunt</u> - a short trip; <u>journal</u> - a diary; <u>journey</u> – a trip (500 years ago a journey was a trip you could make in one day)!

Before U Go

Make a list of clothes & stuff to pack (like this book plus ballpoint pens & color pencils). Write in erasable pencil & start the list way before U leave so U have time to think of everything. Write down names & addresses of people to send post cards to while U R away. Get a compass if U want to know which way is North! Take a book for fun reading. Use a permanent marker, like a Sharpie®, to write on billboard on the cover of your Travel Diary. Put the trip & the year, your name & year, or your camp's name. Give it a couple of days to dry.

Writing Over Pictures

Yikes! Some of U really hate to write on top of a picture. I did, too, until I found out how much fun it is! There are quite a few pages in this book with lines right across the pictures — go ahead and write! Maps have always had writing on them, so don't be shy.

Room 4 U 2 Write

There R 40 1/2 pages with lines 4 writing & if U tend 2 write a lot U can write small, or do extra pages 2 keep in one of the pockets in the back. Also U can cram more in if U use abbreviations of words:

U – you	8 – ate
w/ – with	GR8 – great
w/o – without	L8 – late
& – and	Y – why
@ – at, each	Z – sleep
B – be, bee	$ – money
B4 – before	$$ – pricey
C – sea, see	H2O – water
R – are	♡ – love
2 – to, too	↑ – up
4 – for	↓ – down

Filling Up!

Fill up the pages. Write, draw, or paste in pictures. U can also draw little pictures in with your writing. Or make teensy photocopies of real stuff and paste them in.

Pockets 4 Stuff

The three pockets are for <u>Photos</u>, <u>Post cards</u>, and blow-away, throw-away mementos called <u>Ephemera</u> (here today gone tomorrow). Put little things in an envelope, or tie a ribbon around the pockets, or don't turn the book upside down!

The Longgg Map

With a map you can see your whole trip in one glance. Use the four-page fold-out map to write in the names of the important places U go. Stick in stickers or cut-out pictures. On the back of the map, fill in the signs with anything U like.

Where I'm Going: _____

When I Leave: _____

When I return: _____

Who's going: _____

What I'll ride in or on: _____

Why I'm going on this trip: _____

The Bay of Fun

Four Isle Bay

Mermaid Bay

What Time It Is/Was When I . . .

Left Home

Saw the First

Had First Meal

Got to main Destination

Saw the First Star

Got Back Home!

Exact moment I knew I was Having a Good Time!!

NORTH

SPLIT ENDS
BAY

EAST

SOUTH

"The use of travelling is to regulate imagination by reality, and, instead of thinking how things may be, to see them as they are." Samuel Johnson.

"I never travel without my diary. One should always have something sensational to read in the train." Oscar Wilde

WAG
OCEAN

BARK
BAY

"It takes all sorts
to make a world."
Old Proverb

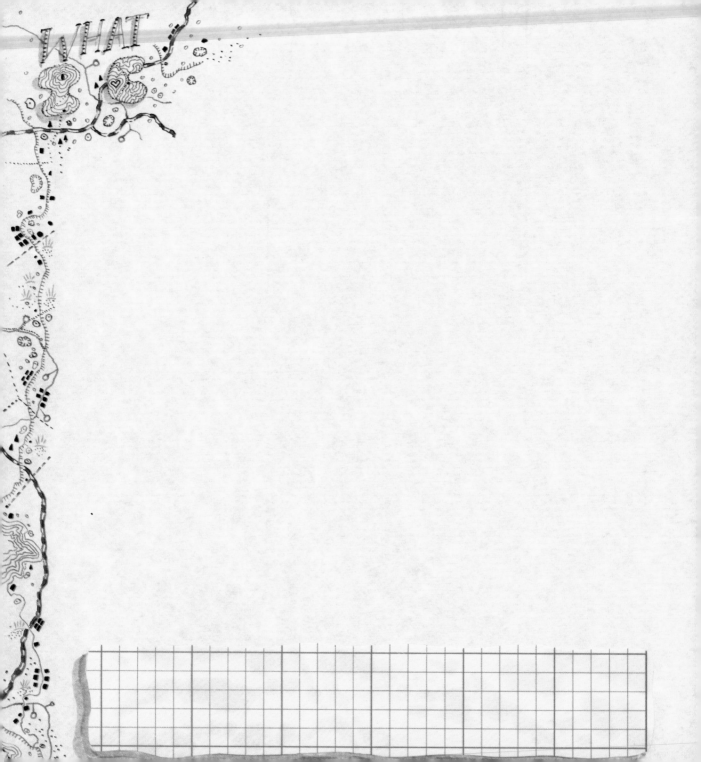

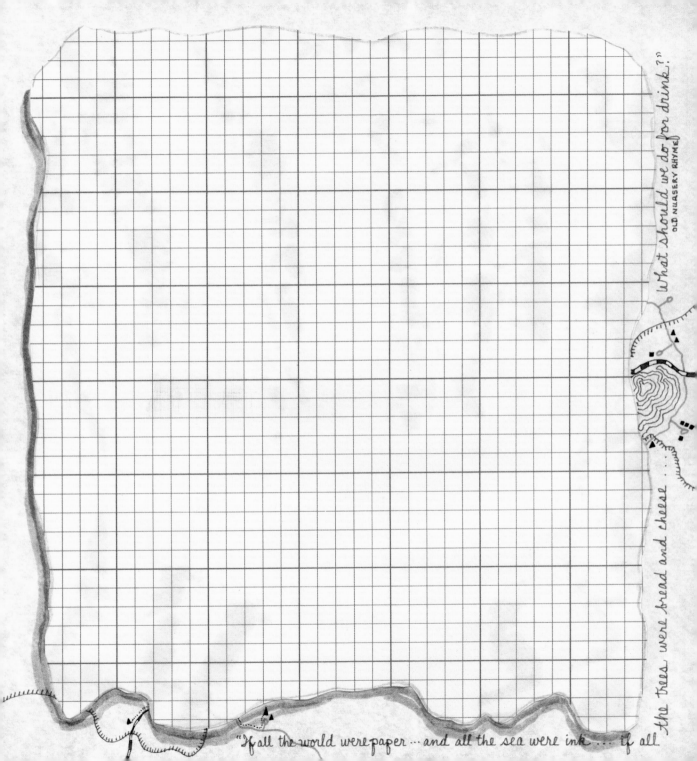

"If all the world were paper ... and all the sea were ink ... if all the trees were bread and cheese ... What should we do for drink?"

OLD NURSERY RHYME

"Make short the miles with talk and smiles." *Old proverb*

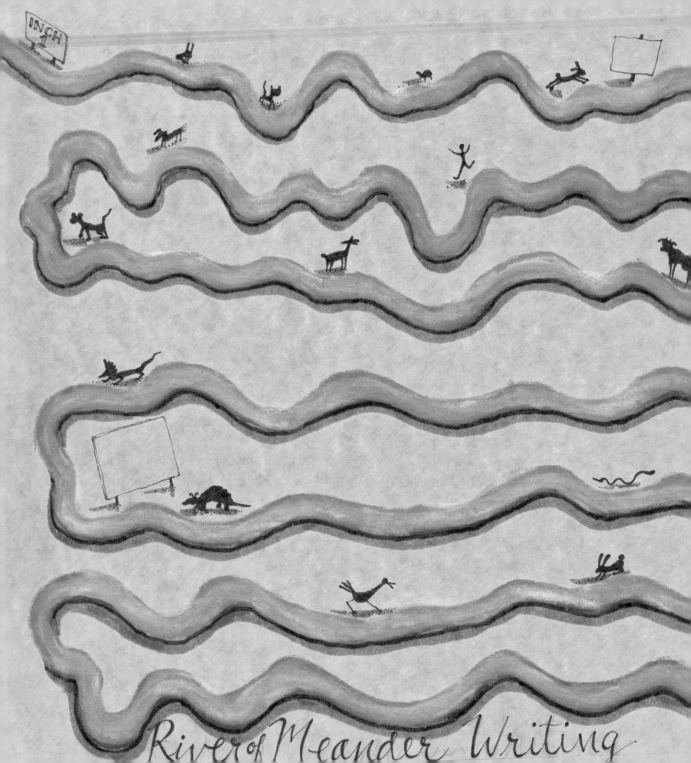

River of Meander Writing

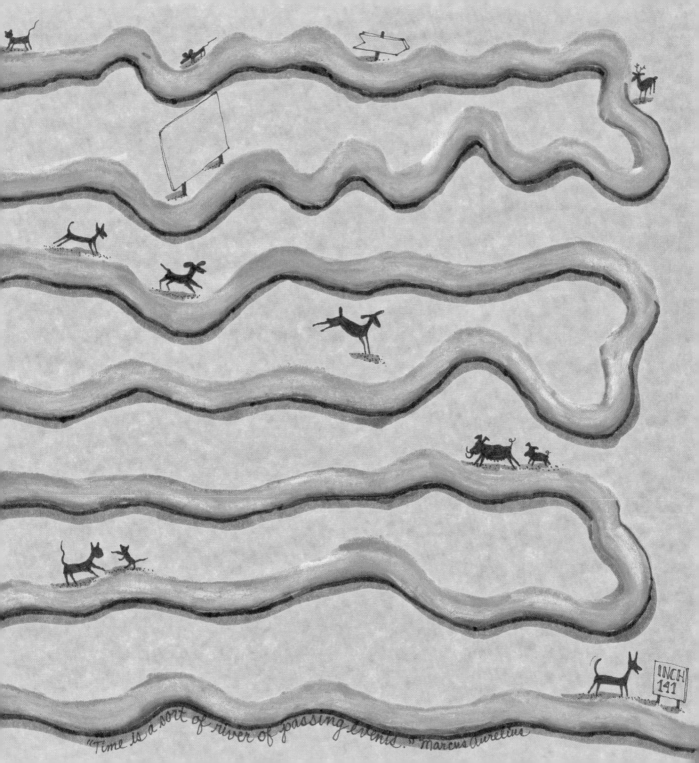

"Time is a sort of river of passing events." Marcus Aurelius

"...raveling is seeing"
Cynthia Ozick

"We own the right of roaming. and the world is wide." Bertha Rundle

"My Book
and Heart
Shall never part."
New England Primer

"You've been out in the sun long enough, dear!"

"The  is going to shine down on me in some faraway place." Mahalia Jackson

"The world is a wheel, and it will all come round right." Benjamin Disraeli

"They that travel
far know much."
Old Proverb

"No road is long when you're in good company." Old proverb

MAP NOT TO SCALE

"Don't forget the bridges you crossed: you may have to go back that way again." Gladys Knight's mother

"The world goes up and the world goes down, And the sunshine follows the rain;
And yesterday's sneer and yesterday's frown Can never come over again." Charles Kingsley

"There are two worlds; the world that we can measure with line and rule, and the world that we feel with our hearts and imagination." Leigh Hunt

"Behold the world, how it is whirled round..." *Sir John Davies*

A Poem About My Trip.

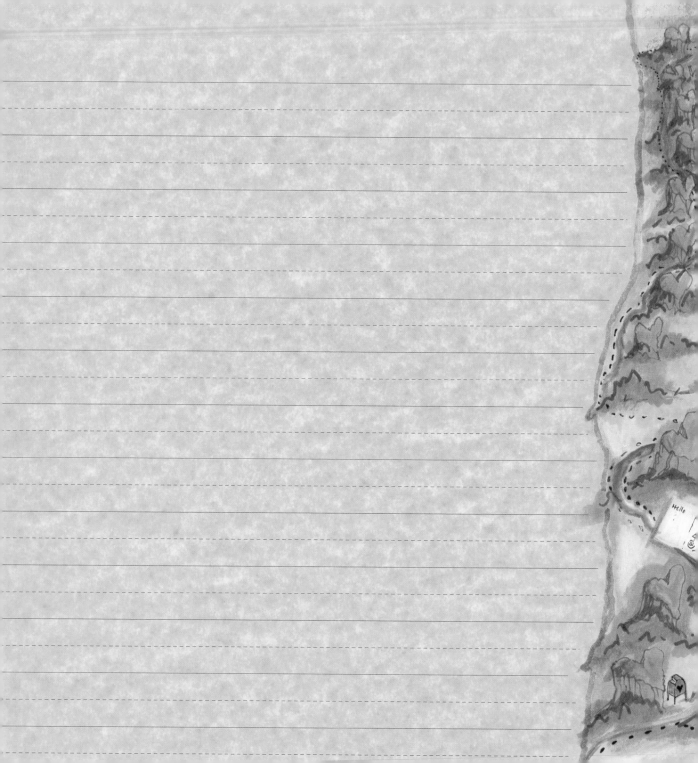

"One day with life and heart, is more than time enough to find a world." James Russell

GOOD TRIP FOOD

REALLY GOOD FOOD !!

STUFF I NEVER ATE
BEFORE ... BUT LIKED!!

Dessert I Loved

Place Names

SOUVENIR LIST

GIFTS

_____
_____
_____
_____
_____
_____

HOW MUCHO MOOLAH I HAVE 2 SPEND

_____

HOW MUCHO I SPENT

_____
_____
_____
_____
_____
_____
_____

"One cannot collect all the beautiful shells on the beach."
Anne Morrow Lindbergh

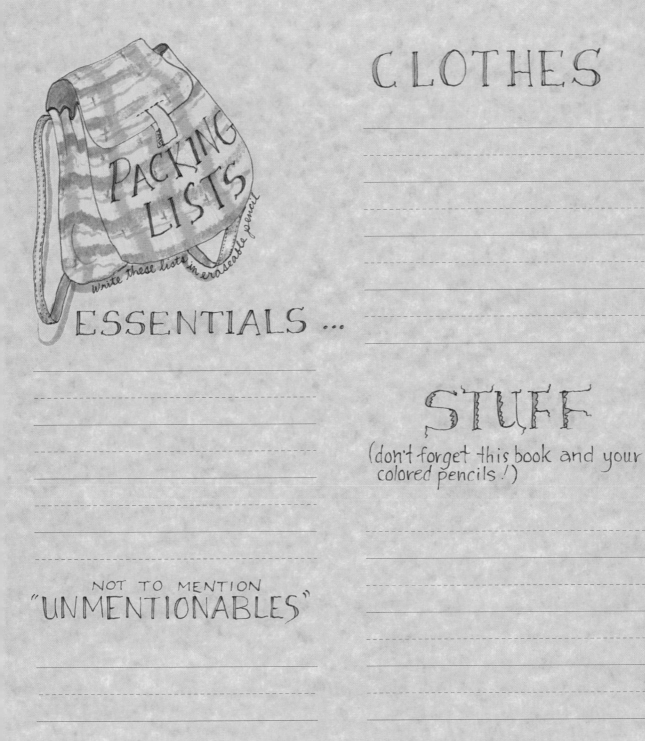

PACKING LISTS

write these lists in eraseable pencil

CLOTHES

ESSENTIALS ...

NOT TO MENTION "UNMENTIONABLES"

STUFF

(don't forget this book and your colored pencils!)

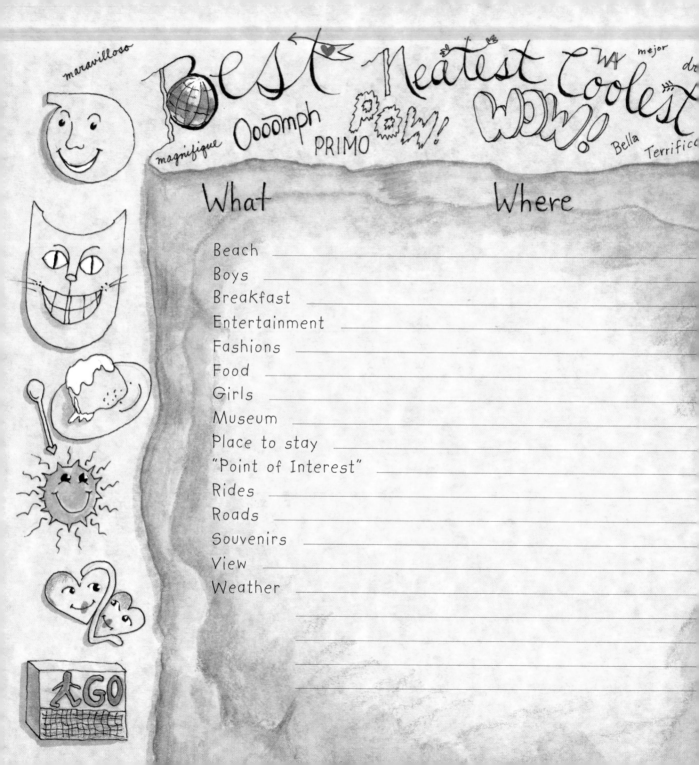

maravilloso

Best ← Neatest Coolest
magnifique Ooooomph POW! WOW! Bella Terrifico
PRIMO mejor

What   ## Where

Beach _____
Boys _____
Breakfast _____
Entertainment _____
Fashions _____
Food _____
Girls _____
Museum _____
Place to stay _____
"Point of Interest" _____
Rides _____
Roads _____
Souvenirs _____
View _____
Weather _____
_____
_____
_____
_____

GO

Worst Dumbest Yuckiest

plus mal

lo peor

mauvais   rotto

(or DumWorst)

URPiest   YECCHH!   Arghh   grosero   Dull

horroroso   brutto

What   ## Where

Beach _____

Boys _____

Breakfast _____

Entertainment _____

Fashions _____

Food _____

Girls _____

Museum _____

Place to stay _____

"Point of Interest" _____

Rides _____

Roads _____

Souvenirs _____

View _____

Weather _____

_____

_____

_____

_____

STOP

Bumper Stickers I C

WHIRLED PEAS

↗ This one I made up! ↑

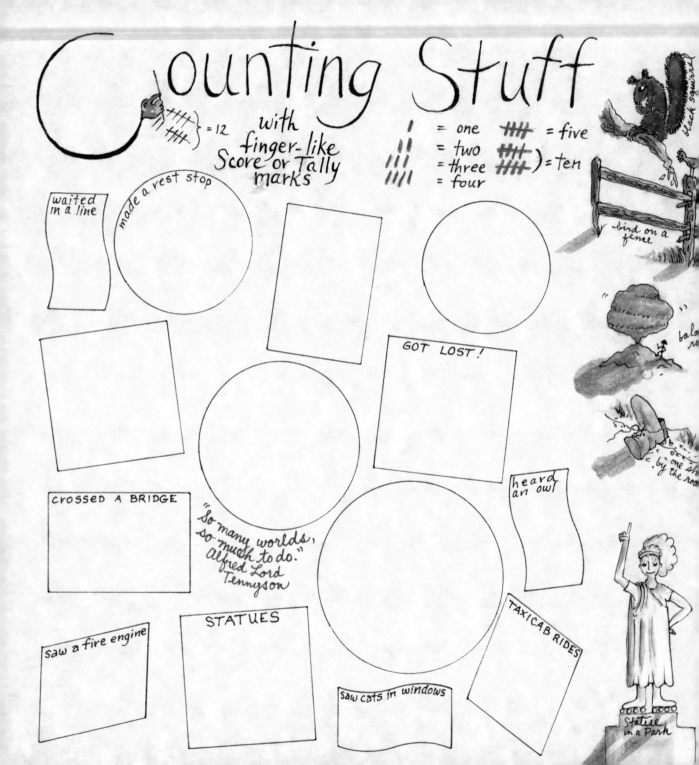

Counting Stuff

with finger-like Score or Tally marks

 = 12

| | = one
||| = two
||| = three
|||| = four
 = five
 = ten

black squirrel

bird on a fence

"So many worlds, so much to do."
Alfred Lord Tennyson

waited in a line

made a rest stop

GOT LOST!

heard an owl

CROSSED A BRIDGE

saw a fire engine

STATUES

saw cats in windows

TAXICAB RIDES

Statue in a Park

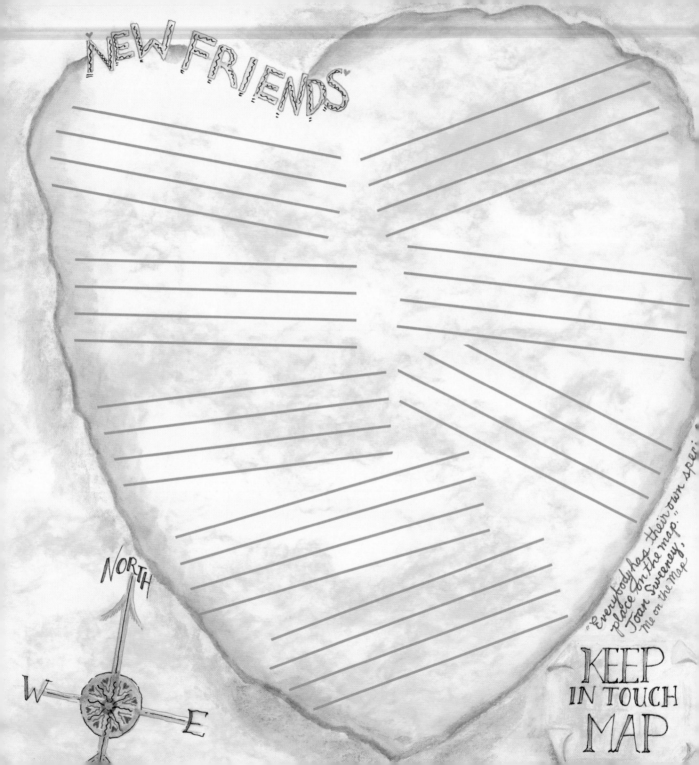

NEW FRIENDS

NORTH

W   E

"Everybody has their own special place on the map."
— Joan Sweeney,
Me on the Map

KEEP IN TOUCH MAP

Autographs

Addresses of Friends and family

ooh! I'm glad 2 B home!

P.S. you can send cards home to yourself + put in a pocket later

Post Cards
to send
and to
keep

Dear Tuffy,
I am sorry we had
u at the neighbors. Hey!
if they R neighbors
they must eat like
horses, so Tuffy if
you look pretty little
maybe they will
give you BIG portions.
Love, M. Tuftim

Tuff Feline
1412 PARK AV.
Baltimore MD.
2 1 2 1 7

U at [house] am having a
O.k.P.! C U soon
-ific

for more
THERE IS A HAPPY LAND
After you've seen
helps shorten long trips.
FUN
its Peak

TIC

ADMIT
ONE

8654021

18136744

KET

oTR-41

Ephemera ~
(F·M·R·A·)

Stuff that most people just throw away . . . . but

MONTGO.
CO.

WESTOWN
RD.

ALLSVILLE
RD.

28

HUNTER
RD.

Enl.
area
MO

© You have yearning for perfection.

FERRY
RD.

109

0   3

MILES

Miller

Hart I   14

13   8

Obstr
Fish Haven
(auth min 11 ft)

17   14

14

13

F 105ft

13   7

F1 G 4sec
Ra Ref

11   15

14   4

people
like us
keep because
it reminds us
of a moment
in a
day!

you'll find

Lost

VID BERKE

· ticket stubs ·maps
· drawings on a
luggage tags paper napkin
· brochures ·hotel
stationery
·labels ·price tags
·newspaper clippings
·stuff you find that can·be
taped to a piece of
paper....or
photocopied

PLACE

a Hill   a Mesa

Two Mountains   and a Valley

A Landmark

They said turn left at the "big heart"

An Oasis   a Dune

A Desert

A Desert Island

The Horizon ↑

A Bay

This "body of water" is a lake or an ocean or a sea